Contents

1 Basic approach

The approach behind Abacus is based on a partnership between Teacher and Pupil. The process can be summarised as

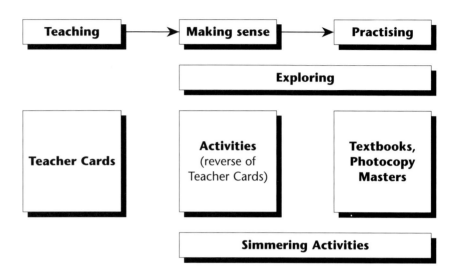

Teaching

At the heart of this approach is the teaching process. The mathematical content is divided into units, each of which is centred around a piece of directed teaching. We believe that it is the quality of the teaching that shapes the quality of pupils' subsequent work in each unit.

Abacus therefore aims to provide maximum support to you the teacher in this endeavour through the use of the Teacher Cards. These build a sound basis of material assistance with either class or group teaching. Abacus is unique in the support it offers to teachers wanting to deliver quality teaching to pupils in their class.

Making sense

Abacus recognises that it is essential that pupils make sense of what they have been taught. In order to do this, they must make that knowledge their own. There are many ways in which pupils make sense of mathematical ideas. Traditionally, practical activities, often utilising structural apparatus, have been seen to play a crucial role in helping pupils to make sense of mathematics.

Abacus provides many practical activities on the back of each Teacher Card, as well as a Resource Pack to accompany them. Additional activities are included in the Numeracy Support and Challenge Books. However, practical activities are not the only answer. The importance of stories, investigations, puzzles and games is also well established. Abacus includes these through the activities, the Photocopy Masters and the book of Simmering Activities.

In addition, each Resource Pack contains games that match specified teaching points.

Practising

Many skills do require an element of practice, particularly those that we want the pupils to have on 'automatic pilot'. Skills such as 'recall of the multiples of five' need to be routines which pupils have at their disposal without having to think about them.

Traditionally, mathematics schemes have provided for the practice of skills through pupils' individual workbooks and textbooks. Abacus certainly provides these, but does not rely solely upon the use of workbooks and textbooks to deliver the practice element of the curriculum. There are many 'simmering' activities whose function is specifically oral practice of particular skills. Verbal mathematics is a crucial part of Abacus and both the activities on the Teacher Cards and the Simmering Activities reflect this focus.

In addition, there are Photocopy Masters that provide extra practice of particularly important skills, for those situations where you feel they are needed. Specific support for children with special educational need is included in the Numeracy Support Book.

Exploring

Children need to explore the mathematics they have learned, and to experience the creative side of mathematics. Too often in the past, mathematics has been a 'byword for boredom'. Not with Abacus. Throughout the Textbooks, there are 'Explores' and other open-ended activities that focus upon mathematical processes. They allow for the element of creativity and subjective interpretation. Abacus enables you to provide the pupils with a stimulating diet of exploratory mathematical activities.

Using and Applying Mathematics

Throughout every aspect of Abacus, pupils are required to use and to apply their mathematical skills. In this sense, AT1 may be said to be an integrated part of the programme, rather than an 'add-on' component. It is possible to trace the development of specific skills in this context through the different strands of Abacus.

Basic approach

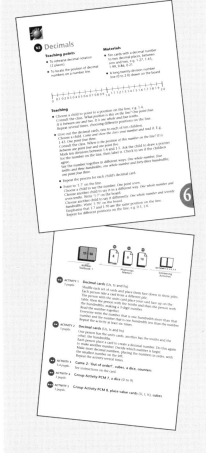

Developing pupils' powers of reasoning and decision-making

The pupils follow up the initial teaching input and activities using the Textbook pages and selected Photocopy Masters. Throughout these pages they will encounter 'Explore' activities, where they are required to think something through for themselves. It is often appropriate to encourage pupils to work in pairs on these activities, so that they can talk about the different possibilities and discuss their reasons for and against a particular line of enquiry.

Similarly, many of the activities on the reverse of the Teacher Cards involve the pupils in the same sort of reasoning process. In order to complete these tasks, the pupils, working in small groups, need to select the appropriate mathematics and organise their work, overcoming any problems that arise.

Using appropriate mathematical language

The practice and reinforcement materials in Abacus have been carefully graded in terms of the mathematical vocabulary they develop and require. Key terminology is highlighted throughout, and the Teacher Cards provide teachers with explicit advice as to the appropriate vocabulary at each stage. In both the teaching and the learning strategies, there is an emphasis on 'reading' mathematical sentences. Much attention is paid to the development in reading sentences such as $15 \div 3 = 5$, from 'shared among' to 'divided by'.

The activities that follow the teaching have been designed to allow pupils to use the mathematical vocabulary provided as they talk through the tasks or solve the problems presented. Often, these activities present the pupils with mathematical questions, which in turn lead onto further questions formulated by the pupils themselves. Necessarily, the activities provide a situation in which pupils discuss their work in a variety of different mathematical contexts.

Predicting and generalising

The Textbooks present each mathematical topic in a series of different contexts. Frequently, the mathematics appears in a more 'embedded' form and the pupils are required to use the context in solving problems. This encourages the pupils to see beyond one simple formulation of each piece of mathematics. The Explore sections in the Textbooks continue this 'thinking through' process, encouraging the pupils to investigate a particular aspect of that mathematical topic. Each Explore provides a mathematical investigation or an open-ended mathematical problem to discuss and solve. In the course of this the pupils will certainly make predictions, and test these out. On occasion they may also generalise and produce a more universal statement.

Basic approach

The activities on the reverse of the Teacher Cards also provide a context in which pupils will investigate a mathematical idea or problem. They will be encouraged to generate or observe mathematical patterns and then to generalise from these. Through both the Explore sections in the Textbooks, and the activities, the more creative and playful aspects of mathematics are encouraged.

Mental maths

Throughout Abacus particular attention is paid to the development of mental skills in numeracy. At all stages in the programme, the pupils are taught mental strategies before moving on to use written algorithms. They are encouraged to use techniques such as adding ten, counting on in tens or multiples of ten, adding to the next ten and known number facts. The development and practice of these strategies is a specific feature of both the teaching and learning materials.

Teacher Cards

These have been structured to ensure that specific mental strategies are in place as they are needed at each stage. For example, pupils are shown how to count on in tens or multiples of ten in order to facilitate their addition of 2-digit numbers. Abacus prioritises techniques which enable pupils to become numerically fluent, and to perform number operations mentally with confidence and enthusiasm.

Activities

Many of the activities on the reverse of the Teachers Cards draw upon those strategies and techniques that have been introduced in the teaching. These enable pupils to practise their mental operations in the context of a practical rather than a written task. This is a very important aspect of the development of mental fluency in number.

Explores in the Textbooks

These sections provide an opportunity for the pupils to develop their own personal 'short cuts' and individual techniques, and to make those they have been taught their own. The Explore sections involve some creative mathematical thinking and it is the mental agility required to solve these problems that enables pupils to personalise their mental strategies.

Simmering Activities

This component of Abacus is unique in that it targets solely and wholly the development of real numerical fluency. By keeping mental strategies 'simmering', that is practising these on a 'little and often' basis, pupils retain those techniques and strategies which they would otherwise be inclined to forget. The short activities for the whole class which are provided in the Simmering Activities are a major factor in the development of pupils' mental maths skills.

② The materials

		ABACUS 4	ABACUS 5	ABACUS 6
Year		4/P5	5/P6	6/P7
Approx Age		8 to 9	9 to 10	10 to 11
TEACHING		Abacus 4 Teacher Cards	Abacus 5 Teacher Cards	Abacus 6 Teacher Cards
MAKING SENSE		Abacus 4 Resource Pack	Abacus 5 Resource Pack	Abacus 6 Resource Pack
PRACTISING		Abacus 4 Number Textbook 1 Number Textbook 2 Shape, Data and Measures Textbook	Abacus 5 Number Textbook 1 Number Textbook 2 Shape, Data and Measures Textbook	Abacus 6 Number Textbook 1 Number Textbook 2 Shape, Data and Measures Textbook
		Abacus 4 Photocopy Masters	Abacus 5 Photocopy Masters	Abacus 6 Photocopy Masters
			Abacus 3/4 Simmering Activities	Abacus 5/6 Simmering Activities
		Abacus 4 Numeracy Support Book Challenge Book	Abacus 5 Numeracy Support Book Challenge Book	Abacus 6 Numeracy Support Book Challenge Book
CURRICULUM SUPPORT Separate Scottish and Northern Ireland versions	England and Wales	Abacus 4 Teachers' Book	Abacus 5 Teachers' Book	Abacus 6 Teachers' Book
	Scotland and Northern Ireland	Abacus 4 Scotland Teachers' Book Abacus 4 Northern Ireland Teachers' Book	Abacus 5 Scotland Teachers' Book Abacus 5 Northern Ireland Teachers' Book	Abacus 6 Scotland Teachers' Book Abacus 6 Northern Ireland Teachers' Book

Teacher Cards

These are the heart of the whole scheme. Within each unit the Teacher Card details how you introduce and develop the mathematical content in the lesson (either with the whole class or a group). On the back of the card there are suggested activities for the pupils to undertake in small groups, using a range of materials. The card also identifies relevant Textbook pages, Photocopy Masters and Simmering Activities. All components within the units have been written to cover a wide range of ability within the class. Not all activities need to be done by all pupils.

The Teacher Cards are divided into two sets, Number, and Shape, Data and Measures. A suggested order of cards, both within each set and between the sets, is identified for you but you may wish to produce your own. In this way Abacus allows you to provide a programme suitably differentiated to meet the needs of each pupil within your class.

Abacus 6 contains five Number 'Recap' cards. These are extra Teacher Cards, providing revision of key skills. They precede the appropriate core unit, so for example, before N1: Place-value in large numbers, there is a Recap Card R1: Place-value in 3- and 4-digit numbers. These cards can be used with any pupils who are not quite ready for the core work, to give them extra consolidation before embarking on the core teaching, activities and Textbook pages. For some units, you may decide to use the Recap with the whole class.

Each Recap card has activities, Textbook pages and Photocopy Masters associated with it.

Teaching objectives clearly stated

Clear guidance on introducing and teaching the mathematical concepts and skills.

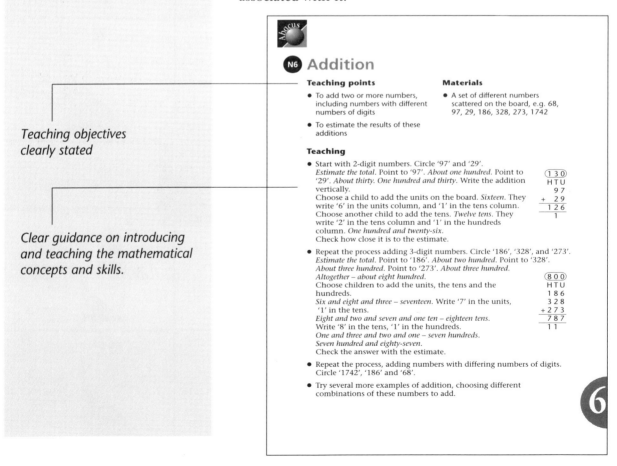

The materials

Cross-references to the Textbook pages, Photocopy Masters and relevant Simmering Activities.

A range of practical activities for consolidation and practice.

Differentiation – a simple code shows the level of difficulty of each activity and Photocopy Master:

- ● Basic work
- ●● For all children
- ●●● Enrichment and extension

Activities

Each Teacher Card identifies a range of activities which pupils should undertake following your teaching with the whole class or group. All activities are designed to be set up easily and quickly. Some use materials from the Resource Pack (e.g. number cards, place-value cards), others require no special resources.

The activities are for use with groups of pupils and span the whole ability range in the class allowing suitable differentiation to take place. Some activities offer support to those pupils needing more basic work and consolidation. Others provide enrichment and extension for those needing more demanding work.

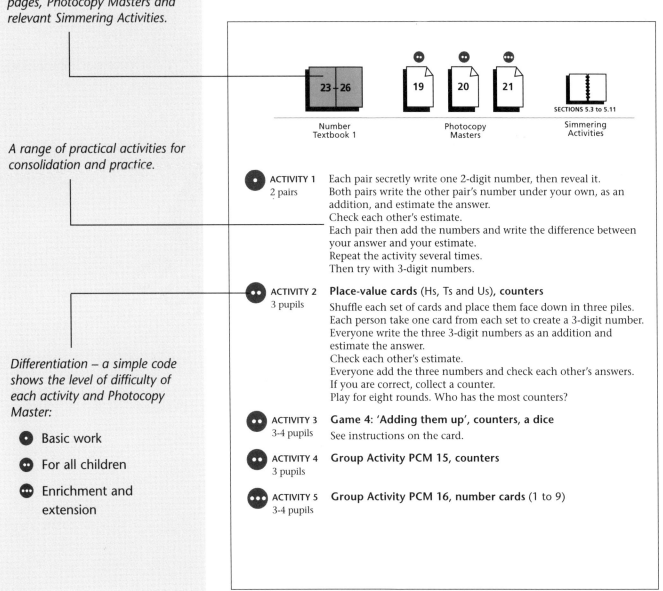

Number Textbook 1: 23–26

Photocopy Masters: 19, 20, 21

Simmering Activities: SECTIONS 5.3 to 5.11

ACTIVITY 1
2 pairs

Each pair secretly write one 2-digit number, then reveal it.
Both pairs write the other pair's number under your own, as an addition, and estimate the answer.
Check each other's estimate.
Each pair then add the numbers and write the difference between your answer and your estimate.
Repeat the activity several times.
Then try with 3-digit numbers.

ACTIVITY 2
3 pupils

Place-value cards (Hs, Ts and Us), **counters**

Shuffle each set of cards and place them face down in three piles.
Each person take one card from each set to create a 3-digit number.
Everyone write the three 3-digit numbers as an addition and estimate the answer.
Check each other's estimate.
Everyone add the three numbers and check each other's answers.
If you are correct, collect a counter.
Play for eight rounds. Who has the most counters?

ACTIVITY 3
3-4 pupils

Game 4: 'Adding them up', counters, a dice
See instructions on the card.

ACTIVITY 4
3 pupils

Group Activity PCM 15, counters

ACTIVITY 5
3-4 pupils

Group Activity PCM 16, number cards (1 to 9)

The materials

Resource Pack

The Resource Pack contains specially produced materials for you to use at relevant stages within the scheme, games that match specified teaching points, photocopy masters for group activities and the means for you to create other necessary materials. The Pack contains multiple sets of number cards, place-value cards etc., so that more than one group of pupils can work on the same activity at the same time. Each Teacher Card clearly identifies the resources from the pack and other materials needed for the practical activities covered on the card. Abacus does not need additional materials other than those found in a normal classroom. A full list of requirements for this year of the scheme is given in Appendix (i) on page 43.

Textbooks

There are three Textbooks in Abacus 6, two for Number and one for Shape, Data and Measures. Each page offers consolidation of the practical work covered with you and gives evidence of the pupil's progress through the scheme.

The instructions on the pages are contained in speech bubbles. This has the dual function of keeping text to a minimum, as well as aiding readability. Key mathematical vocabulary is reinforced throughout.

Generally the first question on each page is done for the pupils. A recording box on each page shows the pupils exactly how to set out their work.

On each page the appropriate key skill, practice or concept is identified for assessment purposes. A key feature of certain pages is the inclusion of 'Explores' that provide additional activities usually with an investigational or process skills focus.

All answers to the questions in the textbooks, and guidance on the Explores are found in the Answer Book.

Simmering Activities

Relevant mental activities, algorithms, quick-recalls, games and other activities are contained in the Simmering Activities book, and referred to on the relevant Teacher Cards. The activities require little or no preparation and are brief enough to be done in just a few minutes – at registration or in the dinner queue. Once introduced the activity must be used regularly to allow the key concept, skill or practice covered by the activity to keep simmering.

5.7 Adding near multiples of 100

Abacus 6
N6, N10

- Write on the board: 199, 499, 799, 599, 999, 299, 699, 99, 399, 899.
  Point to a number and ask the children to read it, e.g. *one hundred and ninety-nine*. Next ask them what this number is 'nearly'. They shout: *two hundred*.
  Continue for each number.

- Write 199 on the board. Choose a child and say a 3-digit number, e.g. 361 They add 199 and say the answer. If correct, that child chooses another and says a 3-digit number, e.g. 758. That child adds 199 and says the answer. Continue around the class.
  Each child has three chances to make a mistake or hesitate.

- **A dice**
  Divide the class into four teams and draw four columns on the board, one for each team. Each team chooses a 3-digit number and writes it in their column. Each team throws the dice and creates a number by multiplying by 100 and subtracting one, e.g. throw 3 make 299. They add to their first number and write the answer in their column. The team with an answer closest to 999 scores a point.
  Play again.

17

The materials

Photocopy Masters

These sheets contain practical activities to enhance the pupil's learning and are identified on the Teacher Cards. They include:

● More work for reinforcement
● Extension and enhancement material.

The Photocopy Masters are coded in the same way as the Teacher Card activities, i.e.:

● Basic work
●● For all children
●●● Enrichment and extension

Name _____

Percentages

Write each fraction as a percentage.

1. $\frac{1}{10} = \boxed{}$ %   2. $\frac{1}{100} = \boxed{}$ %

3. $\frac{1}{20} = \boxed{}$ %   4. $\frac{1}{2} = \boxed{}$ %

5. $\frac{1}{4} = \boxed{}$ %   6. $\frac{1}{5} = \boxed{}$ %

7. $\frac{3}{10} = \boxed{}$ %   8. $\frac{3}{4} = \boxed{}$ %

9. $\frac{2}{5} = \boxed{}$ %   10. $\frac{1}{50} = \boxed{}$ %

11. $\frac{11}{20} = \boxed{}$ %   12. $\frac{1}{25} = \boxed{}$ %

13. $\frac{9}{10} = \boxed{}$ %   14. $\frac{4}{5} = \boxed{}$ %

15. $\frac{17}{50} = \boxed{}$ %   16. $\frac{7}{10} = \boxed{}$ %

17. $\frac{6}{10} = \boxed{}$ %   18. $\frac{2}{50} = \boxed{}$ %

19. $\frac{6}{25} = \boxed{}$ %   20. $\frac{3}{5} = \boxed{}$ %

54

The materials

Numeracy Support Book

The Numeracy Support Book is aimed specifically at those pupils who are having difficulty with their number work, where their level of attainment across a range of numerical topics is significantly behind the rest of the class. The book provides practical assistance for teachers involved in matching appropriate tasks to the targets on individual education plans.

The book outlines the skills, the teaching strategies, the activities and the follow-up work appropriate in this context, and is divided into sections under mathematical skills headings (e.g. adding tens, multiplication facts).

Each section provides a step-by-step progression of teaching strategies to help pupils understand and assimilate a particular piece of mathematics. A range of tactics for each topic is provided, along with a number of straightforward practical activities. Follow-up work in the form of photocopy masters provides carefully graded examples of the specific numerical skills.

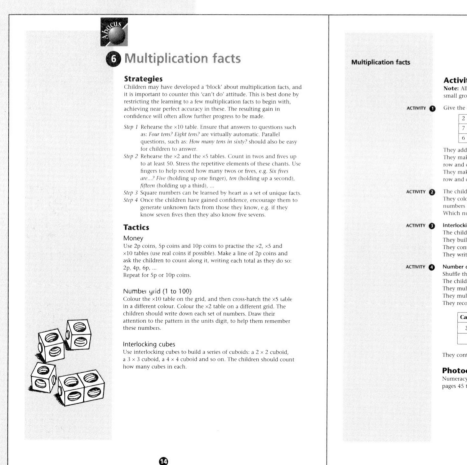

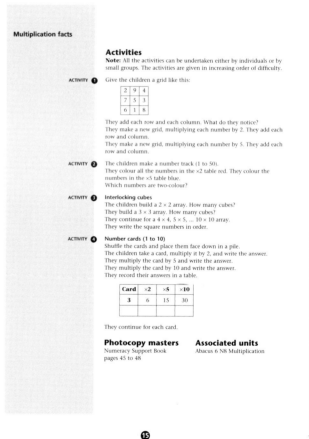

The materials

Challenge Book

The Challenge Book is a resource for providing additional challenging mathematics to that already included in the Abacus 6 materials, to further extend the more-able pupils.

There are numerous opportunities, within the core of Abacus 6, for teachers to select tasks appropriate for the more-able child. The Challenge Book provides additional suggestions for such opportunities with a range of structured, challenging and purposeful activities.

The book is divided into sections of mathematical topics relating to Units or groups of Units within Abacus 6. The suggested Challenges provide the teacher with a wide selection of activities within each Unit for the more-able children.

The challenges cover both mathematical depth (in which children extend their study of a particular piece of mathematics, but at a **higher** level) and breadth (in which children seek to broaden their understanding of a piece of mathematics at the **same** level). The suggested activities are often open-ended and of a problem-solving nature, geared towards the development of the children's process skills. It is anticipated that this material will develop the child's ability to 'use and apply mathematics' at a higher level.

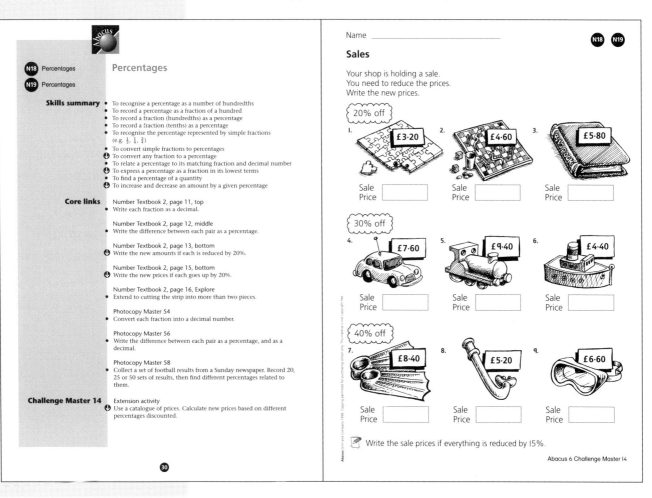

Percentages

N18 Percentages
N19 Percentages

Skills summary
- To recognise a percentage as a number of hundredths
- To record a percentage as a fraction of a hundred
- To record a fraction (hundredths) as a percentage
- To record a fraction (tenths) as a percentage
- To recognise the percentage represented by simple fractions (e.g. $\frac{1}{2}$, $\frac{1}{4}$, $\frac{3}{4}$)
- To convert simple fractions to percentages
- To convert any fraction to a percentage
- To relate a percentage to its matching fraction and decimal number
- To express a percentage as a fraction in its lowest terms
- To find a percentage of a quantity
- To increase and decrease an amount by a given percentage

Core links
Number Textbook 2, page 11, top
- Write each fraction as a decimal.

Number Textbook 2, page 12, middle
- Write the difference between each pair as a percentage.

Number Textbook 2, page 13, bottom
- Write the new amounts if each is reduced by 20%.

Number Textbook 2, page 15, bottom
- Write the new prices if each goes up by 20%.

Number Textbook 2, page 16, Explore
- Extend to cutting the strip into more than two pieces.

Photocopy Master 54
- Convert each fraction into a decimal number.

Photocopy Master 56
- Write the difference between each pair as a percentage, and as a decimal.

Photocopy Master 58
- Collect a set of football results from a Sunday newspaper. Record 20, 25 or 50 sets of results, then find different percentages related to them.

Challenge Master 14
Extension activity
- Use a catalogue of prices. Calculate new prices based on different percentages discounted.

Name _____

N18 **N19**

Sales

Your shop is holding a sale.
You need to reduce the prices.
Write the new prices.

20% off

1. £3·20   2. £4·60   3. £5·80

Sale Price ____   Sale Price ____   Sale Price ____

30% off

4. £7·60   5. £9·40   6. £4·40

Sale Price ____   Sale Price ____   Sale Price ____

40% off

7. £8·40   8. £5·20   9. £6·60

Sale Price ____   Sale Price ____   Sale Price ____

Write the sale prices if everything is reduced by 15%.

Abacus 6 Challenge Master 14

Assessment Grid

An easy-to-use individual assessment recording system is included in Appendix (iii), pages 47 to 52 of this handbook. This covers Key Stage 2 of the National Curriculum and follows on from the complementary system for Key Stage 1 that is used in Abacus R, 1 and 2.

Within each box on the grid there is a key statement of the form:

I can...

add and subtract decimals to 2 places.
6N10, 11, 12

and an indication of where the pupil should be able to do this successfully within the scheme, in this case when doing Teacher Cards N10, N11 or N12 in Abacus 6.

You will know this by working with the pupil.

In general:
you look, you observe,
you listen, you discuss,
you read...
you assess.
In this way assessment is an integral part of Abacus involving the pupil, the teacher, any other adult working with the pupil, and the parent.

The inclusion of whole-class management and differentiation strategies within Abacus means that this ongoing assessment can be immediately used to inform future planning.

③ Using Abacus

Classroom management

For each unit of work the Teacher Card identifies for you:

- the direct teaching to the whole class or group.
- the assigned tasks for groups and individual pupils covering activities, Textbook pages, Photocopy Masters and Simmering Activities.

In this way you can effectively plan for a class of pupils, large or small, covering a wide range of ability and over different ages. Within each unit of work there are always two elements:

| direct teaching | → followed by → | assigned tasks |

The resulting management is evident from the diagram.

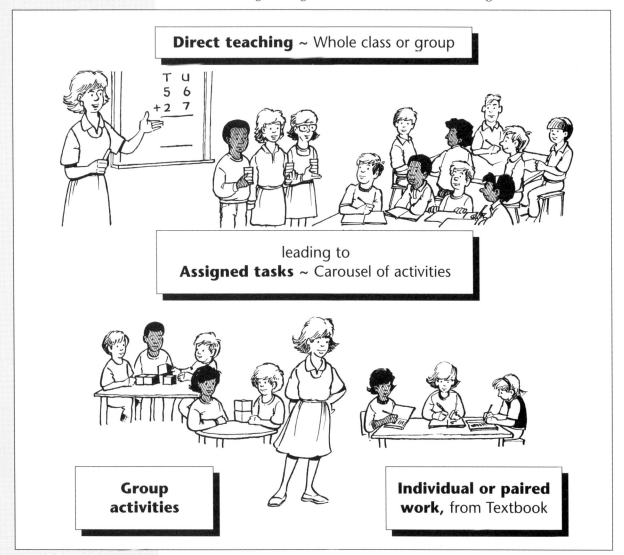

Direct teaching ~ Whole class or group

leading to
Assigned tasks ~ Carousel of activities

Group activities

Individual or paired work, from Textbook

Once Abacus is established in the school, it is possible for you to focus your attention and efforts by starting each mathematical topic by addressing the whole class. Differentiated work and activities then follow this common starting point. This will increase the number of pupils achieving a high standard in mathematics.

In the first year of Abacus, you may find it necessary when doing the active teaching to group the pupils for at least part of their mathematics. We recommend that you have two, or at the most, three groups introducing a topic from the Teacher Card to all the pupils within that group. As the pupils progress through Abacus, the aim is to gradually reduce the differences between the groups so that you can address all the class when starting a topic. This will be achieved over a period, through using the teaching strategies on the Teacher Card together with plenty of oral practice. Once the scheme has been in use for a length of time, pupils entering your class will have used Abacus previously and gained a basic fluency with numbers.

Some schools have decided to adopt mixed age classes throughout the school or for particular ages. Sometimes the numbers of pupils in different year groups lead to this organisation and sometimes it is chosen as the preferred way of working for educational reasons. In this situation, it is easier to treat pupils of the same year as a separate group and plan for each accordingly. You will need to choose the appropriate year group Teacher Cards, introduce the topic to all the pupils within that age group and set up the activities as indicated on the Teacher Card.

In special schools and primary schools with an exaggerated spread of ability, it may be necessary to plan for defined ability groups within the class, but where possible the aim should be to treat the class as a whole, preventing the customary wide spread of ability forming between the most and least able pupils.

Setting up the Activities

The practical activities play a crucial role in helping pupils sort out mathematical concepts in their own minds and start to make sense of them for themselves. The activities on the back of the Teacher Cards are designed to be set up quickly and easily.

If your pupils are not used to working in this way, you will need to introduce them to it gradually:
- work on activities with half the class while the other half work on Textbook pages or Photocopy Masters
- start by choosing one activity that most pupils can tackle. Introduce it to a large group of pupils, before splitting them into smaller groups to do the activity for themselves

Using Abacus

- as pupils become accustomed to this way of working, gradually introduce more than one activity so that perhaps half the class are doing Textbook pages, and half are working on two or three different activities
- do not try to run too many different activities at once

To make the activities easier to manage, many of them use similar formats – both within Abacus 6 and from previous years. Pupils become familiar with the types of activity, and what is expected of them.

The Resource Pack provides multiple sets of many of the resources to enable several groups to work on the same activity at the same time. In addition, photocopy masters of all the resources in the Resource Pack allow you to make additional sets if required.

You will be able to decide the best organisation of groups to suit the needs of the activities used at any time. The following practical suggestions are offered as guidance.

- Limit the size of the group to the number identified on the Teacher Card. Normally form groups by ability but on occasions, some pupils in the class may be used in a peer-tutoring role within the carousel of activities.
- Limit the number of groups to a number you can comfortably manage. Remember more than one group can be doing the same activity. This reduces the number of 'focal points' within the class.
- Pupils will experience a range of tasks within each unit, the actual composition determined by you following the guidance on the Teacher Card. Remember activities are graded according to level of difficulty.
- Other adults can be easily used to assist with the activities.
- You need to judge how much time to allow for different pupils to complete any task. The carousel nature of the tasks provides versatility in your management.

Differentiation

As a result of the simple code on all activities, you are in a position to plan a differentiated range of tasks to match the abilities of all pupils in your class. The diagram illustrates how suitable tasks can be planned.

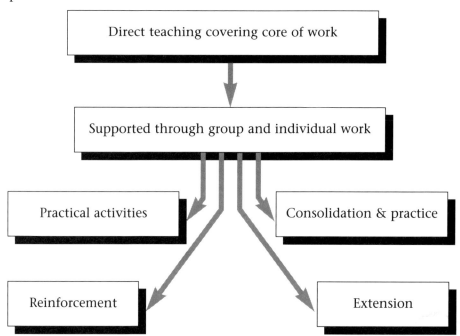

As a consequence of the Code of Practice on Special Educational Needs (SEN) and the production of a register within each school of pupils with SEN, you may have in your class a number of pupils with either an Individual Education Plan or a Statement from your Local Education Authority. Abacus includes a specific range of activities in the Numeracy Support Book (in addition to those identified on the Teacher Card) for these pupils. You may also wish to dip into this book, as necessary, for other pupils who are struggling with their number work.

You may have in your class some pupils who are very able and on occasions need additional challenge, extension and stimulation to that provided within the wide range of activities for each unit. Abacus includes a specific range of activities for these pupils in the Challenge Book. You may dip into this book, as necessary, for other pupils who show particular strengths in a topic.

Using Abacus

To meet fully the needs of all pupils it is necessary to reinforce the built-in task differentiation in Abacus with other strategies.

- Encourage pupils to help one another.
- Provide clear instructions for adult helpers.
- Celebrate pupils' achievement by discussion and display.
- Make assessment criteria very explicit to pupils and parents.
- Allow for differentiated responses to questions and discussion.
- Make learning objectives clear to pupils.
- Intervene sensitively in some activities to extend and reinforce the pupil's learning by careful questioning and guidance.
- Maintain high expectations of all pupils.
- Repeat instructions and explanations.
- Revise frequently.
- Encourage pupils to stay on task.

The problem of differentiation has traditionally been formulated thus:

> Some pupils have, at any one moment, fewer mathematical competencies than other pupils.

↓

> Therefore we provide a different curriculum for each 'group' of pupils, graded according to ability.

↓

> The 'gap' between pupils, in terms of what they can do widens. It is not very great at Year 1 and is much larger at Year 6.

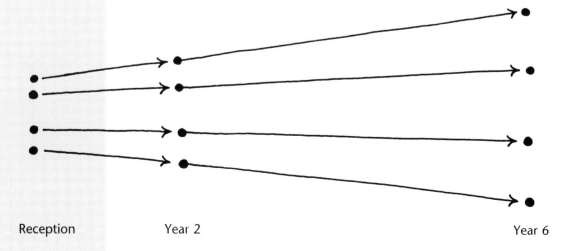

| Reception | Year 2 | Year 6 |

Using Abacus

Abacus has been designed with a new approach to differentiation:

> Each unit of work represents a fresh start. In the main, and with a few exceptions, all the pupils can start each unit together.

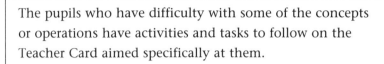

> The pupils who have difficulty with some of the concepts or operations have activities and tasks to follow on the Teacher Card aimed specifically at them.

> The input of the teacher is crucial in helping these pupils. Abacus supports the teacher by:
> - extending/rehearsing the main points raised on the Teacher Card.
> - utilising the activities supplied on the reverse of the card to enable a further teaching input.

Because each unit does represent a new start, a pupil who has had difficulty with, for example, fractions, is not prevented from starting subtraction. Research has shown that mathematics is not all hierarchically structured – it is quite possible that a pupil who has found fractions difficult may have no difficulty with say, taking away tens. Therefore, the model Abacus utilises to cope with differentiation may be depicted more like this:

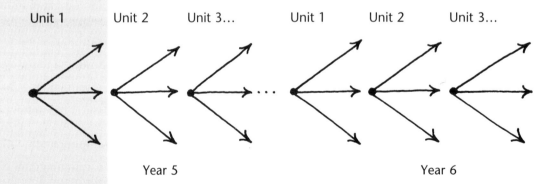

The differences between pupils are not increased by giving them a differentiated diet of mathematical content. The variation in their competencies – how hard they find it to do something – is accommodated by means of differentiated follow-up activities and tasks, with an increased teacher input.

Recording

A record keeping grid is available for each year within Abacus. The grid for this year of the scheme is on pages 44 to 46 of this handbook. This enables you to record which units have been attempted either by the whole class or by individual groups (coded 1, 2, 3, ... to 6).

Calculators

The Abacus team consider the calculator to be a valuable tool in the development of pupils' numerical skills. Consequently, pupils using Abacus are encouraged to develop calculator skills from the early years onwards.

These skills are then used in a variety of different ways and contexts towards the development of high levels of numeracy. These include:
- as a check when practising numerical operations.
- as a stimulus for the development of mental skills.
- as a tool for generating number patterns in order to develop pupils' awareness of pattern.
- as an introduction to working with large numbers.
- as a facilitator for handling realistic data.
- as a means of instigating mathematical investigations.

Each of these uses makes a contribution towards raising the pupils' awareness of number. Use of a calculator is suggested, particularly, in the differentiating practical activities within each Unit.

Information Technology in mathematics

The National Curriculum requires teachers to ensure that Information Technology (IT) is used across all attainment targets of the mathematics curriculum. A variety of IT equipment needs to be included: calculators, programmable robots and computers. Pupils need to be given opportunities to use their mathematical knowledge and skills at levels appropriate to the software used.

Opportunities for pupils to use and apply their mathematical skills may be enhanced by using computers or related technological equipment such as programmable robots. When using a programmable robot they will need to make decisions about which mathematics to use for the task, e.g. which numbers are needed in the context of arbitrary measurement of distance or direction.

The use of a programmable floor robot allows pupils to explore their spatial environment, gaining a feel for movement and an awareness of angle as a measure of turn. They will also develop the language of turtle graphical software such as Logo which they will use within later levels of the National Curriculum.

As far as possible, the contexts for introducing and developing the skills and techniques of representation should arise from the interests of the pupils themselves. The use of IT enables pupils to extract information from their collected data more quickly and so spend more time interpreting and analysing their results.

Teachers should ensure that the software pupils use in data handling complements the skills they have developed within their mathematical experiences, so that they can only access displays that are meaningful to them.

Mathematics in everyday contexts

One of the difficulties with seeing mathematics solely as a school subject is that the pupils can only do mathematics in a school or classroom situation. Abacus follows the recommendations of the National Curriculum in utilising a variety of contexts in which to locate the mathematical examples and practice that the pupils need. These different contexts are provided through:

- the use of games and puzzles as contexts for practising skills. When they are playing a game, or deciding why something works, pupils have a real incentive to 'get the arithmetic right'.
- real-life examples given as practice activities in the Textbooks. Wherever possible, the examples given in the Textbook pages draw upon examples from real-life. Shopping, buying, selling and reducing prices are frequently utilised as situations in which the pupils can practise their skills. Unlike many comparable mathematics schemes, however, Abacus uses real-life and plausible prices, drawing upon objects that the pupils would encounter as purchasers themselves. The scheme generally avoids the use of 'false' pricing – where a book might be 2p or an orange 1p.

Mathematical vocabulary

In order to learn mathematics, pupils need to talk about what they are learning. This means that sometimes the ways in which we express concepts may be very important since they will help the pupils to 'think something through'. The Teacher Cards have been specifically designed to use the terms and vocabulary which are most supportive in this process. Often the cards suggest how a calculation should be read or spoken, as it is performed. The attention to detail in this respect pays off in providing pupils with strategies for actually doing the calculation on their own.

The key phrases and vocabulary highlighted on the Teacher Cards are picked up both through the activities and on the Textbook pages. The titles on these pages use one or two 'key words'. The use of speech bubbles for instructions, whilst keeping reading to a minimum, helps to reinforce these key words.

❹ Organising Abacus 6 units

Abacus units of work

Here the units are listed for you to see clearly the mathematical content and progression within each section and where the content fits in with the programmes of study of the National Curriculum in England and Wales.

There is an implicit commitment to Attainment Target 1: Using and Applying Mathematics throughout Abacus. Within each unit of work the unique combination of

- Teacher Card
- Activities
- Simmering Activities
- Textbook pages
- Explores
- Photocopy Masters
- Games

ensures that pupils are given ample opportunities to:

a) use and apply mathematics in practical tasks, in real-life problems and within mathematics itself

b) explain their thinking to support the development of their reasoning.

Abacus does not contain a separate section with problems and investigations similar to some other schemes. The exploratory approaches reflected in problem solving and investigational work, which is so inherent in AT1, are basic to Abacus. The emphasis on direct teaching followed by assigned tasks and written work enables pupils to use and apply their mathematics at all times and develop these exploratory approaches. They are able to take some responsibility for their learning. They can control the direction of some of their work at their own rate and level. They can organise their own thoughts, ideas and means of communication. They can construct and tackle their own questions. They are able to understand appropriate mathematical language which has always been carefully introduced through the Teacher Card. They can appreciate patterns in their mathematics.

Consequently no explicit references to specific items within the programmes of study from AT1 are listed here.

National Curriculum Programme of Study Key Stage 2 references are coded Attainment Target (1, 2, 3, 4); Section (1, 2, 3, 4, 5); Paragraph (a, b, c, d, e).

Organising Abacus 6 units

Unit	Teaching Point(s)	NC Reference
R1 Number	To recognise the place-value of digits in a 3- or 4-digit number	2.2a
N1 Number	To recognise numbers as large as one million or more	
	To rehearse the place-value of digits in large numbers	2.2a
N2 Decimals	To rehearse recognition of decimal notation (one place)	
	To rehearse ordering decimal numbers (one place)	2.2a, 2.2b
N3 Decimals	To rehearse decimal notation (2 places)	
	To locate the position of decimal numbers on a number line	2.3a, 2.2b
N4 Decimals	To round decimal numbers (2 places) to their nearest whole number and nearest tenth	2.2a
R2 Addition	To recognise and learn addition bonds to 10	
	To recognise addition pairs of multiples of 10 which make 100	2.3c, 2.3d
N5 Addition	To recognise and learn addition bonds to 100	
	To recognise and learn addition bonds to 1000	2.3d
N6 Addition	To add two or more numbers, including numbers with different numbers of digits	
	To estimate the results of these additions	2.3g
N7 Number	To rehearse the position of negative numbers on the number line	
	To add positive and negative numbers	2.2b, 2.3g
N8 Multiplication	To rehearse and consolidate the recognition of multiplication facts up to 10 × 10	2.3c
N9 Division	To rehearse and consolidate the recognition of division facts related to multiplication facts	2.3c, 2.3f
R3 Addition	To add two decimal numbers (1 place), without carrying	2.3e
N10 Addition	To add two decimal numbers (1 place), with carrying	
	To add two decimal numbers (2 places) with carrying	2.3e, 2.3f
N11 Addition	To recognise the next whole number after a decimal number (2 places)	
	To recognise what must be added to a decimal number (2 places) to make the next whole number	2.2b
N12 Subtraction (Red strand)	To subtract one decimal number (2 places) from another with equal adding	2.3g
N12 Subtraction (Blue strand)	To subtract one decimal number (2 places) from another with decomposition	2.3g
N13 Multiplication	To multiply by 10 or 100	
	To multiply by multiples of 10 or 100	2.2a, 2.3d
N14 Multiplication	To multiply a 2-digit number by a 1-digit number	2.3d
N15 Multiplication	To multiply a 2-digit number by a 2-digit number	2.3d
R4 Fractions	To rehearse the recognition of simple fractions	2.2c
N16 Fractions	To recognise mixed fractions	2.2c
N17 Fractions	To rehearse recognition of equivalent fractions	
	To convert fractions to their simplest form	2.2c
N18 Percentages	To rehearse recognition of percentages	
	To relate fractions, decimals and percentages	2.2c, 2.3g
N19 Percentages	To find a percentage of a quantity	
	To recognise everyday uses of percentages	2.2c, 2.3g
N20 Multiples	To understand the term 'multiple'	
	To list the multiples of a number	
	To recognise multiples common to two or more numbers	2.3c
N21 Square numbers	To rehearse the meaning of square numbers	
	To introduce the concept of the square root of a number	2.3c
N22 Factors	To rehearse the meaning of 'factor'	
	To list the factors of a number	
	To recognise prime numbers	2.3c
N23 Division	To recognise numbers which divide by 2, 3, 4, 5, 6 and 10	2.3c
N24 Equations	To introduce the concept of letters to represent unknown numbers in simple equations	
	To solve simple equations by substitution	2.3a, 2.3b
N25 Subtraction (Red strand)	To subtract one whole number from another (with decomposition)	2.3d
N25 Subtraction (Blue strand)	To subtract one whole number from another (with equal adding)	2.3d
R5 Division	To rehearse dividing a 2-digit number by a 1-digit number	2.3d

Organising Abacus 6 units

Unit	Teaching Point(s)	NC Reference
N26 Division	To divide a 3-digit number by a 1-digit number, with remainders	2.3d
N27 Division	To divide a 3-digit number by a 2-digit multiple of 10	2.3d
N28 Problem solving	To solve problems involving different combinations of addition, subtraction, multiplication and division	2.3e, 2.3f
N29 Multiplication	To multiply a decimal number (1 and 2 places) by 10, by 100	2.3d, 2.3g
N30 Multiplication	To multiply a decimal number (1 place) by a 1-digit number	2.3d, 2.3g
N31 Division	To divide a whole number by 10 and 100	2.3d, 2.3g
N32 Division	To divide a decimal number (1 place) by a 1-digit number	2.3d, 2.3g
M1 Length	To introduce the kilometre as a measure To rehearse the relationship between kilometres and metres To introduce the relationship between kilometres and miles	3.4a
M2 Speed	To introduce the concept of speed and its relationship with distance and time	3.4a
M3 Volume and capacity	To consolidate the relationship between different units of volume and capacity	3.4a
M4 Capacity	To link metric and imperial units of capacity	3.4a
M5 Weight	To link metric and imperial units of weight	3.4a
M6 Area	To calculate area by dissecting To find the area of a triangle	3.4c
M7 Area	To find the area of a circle	3.4c
S1 2-d shape	To rehearse the names of common 2-d shapes (including parallelogram and rhombus) To introduce 'trapezium' To introduce 'quadrilateral'	3.2b
S2 2-d shape	To rehearse the names of distances on a circle To rehearse the approximate relationship between diameter and circumference To introduce the 'arc' of a circle	3.2b, 3.4c
S3 3-d shape	To rehearse the names of common 3-d shapes To recognise parallel and perpendicular faces	3.2b, 3.2c
S4 Symmetry	To rehearse the recognition of line symmetry To rehearse the recognition of rotational symmetry To introduce the 'order' of rotational symmetry	3.2c
S5 Angle	To introduce acute, obtuse and reflex angles To recognise acute, obtuse and reflex angles in shapes	3.2b
S6 Angle	To calculate angles, given other angles on a straight line, or at a point	3.3c
S7 Triangles	To introduce acute-angled, and obtuse-angled triangles To sort triangles according to type (acute-angled, obtuse-angled, right-angled)	3.2b, 3.3c
S8 Triangles	To explore the angle sum of a triangle To calculate one angle of a triangle, given the other two	3.3b, 3.2c
S9 Triangles	To introduce names of triangles: isosceles, equilateral, scalene	3.2b
S10 Coordinates	To rehearse reading and plotting points in the first quadrant of a coordinate grid To extend the coordinate grid to four quadrants	4.2b
D1 Pie charts	To introduce a pie chart to represent data To construct and interpret a pie chart	4.2b
D2 Line graphs	To introduce a line graph To construct and interpret a line graph	4.2c
D3 Conversion graphs	To construct and interpret a conversion graph	4.2b
D4 Grouped frequencies	To group continuous data in equal intervals To construct a grouped frequency table To draw and interpret a graph (histogram) based on equal intervals	4.2b
D5 Averages	To rehearse the concept of average To rehearse the calculation of the mean To introduce the median and mode	4.2c
D6 Probability	To introduce the probability scale 0 to 1 To assign probabilities to events	4.3a, 4.3b
D7 Probability	To list all the outcomes of an event To assign probabilities to an event	4.3b, 4.3c

Teaching order of units

The units from Number, and Shape, Data and Measures are given here in one suggested order of teaching. You may prefer to have both Number, and Shape, Data and Measures units developing side by side in which case the association between units can easily be seen from the table. There are other possible routes through the units should you wish to devise your own. In the Shape, Data and Measures Textbook the pages are arranged in topics (length, area, capacity, volume, etc.) allowing you to develop your teaching on a topic basis if you so wish. Abacus is designed to be adaptable, versatile and flexible.

Number	Shapes, Data and Measures
Recap 1 Number	
N1 Number	M1 Length
N2 Decimals	S1 2-d shape
N3 Decimals	
N4 Decimals	S2 2-d shape
Recap 2 Addition	
N5 Addition	M2 Speed
N6 Addition	S3 3-d shape
N7 Number	
N8 Multiplication	M3 Volume and capacity
N9 Division	S4 Symmetry
Recap 3 Addition	
N10 Addition	
N11 Addition	M4 Volume and capacity
N12 Subtraction (Red strand)	S5 Angle
N12 Subtraction (Blue strand)	
N13 Multiplication	
N14 Multiplication	M5 Weight
N15 Multiplication	S6 Angle
Recap 4 Fractions	
N16 Fractions	D1 Pie charts
N17 Fractions	
N18 Percentages	D2 Line graphs
N19 Percentages	S7 Triangles
N20 Multiples	
N21 Square numbers	D3 Conversion graphs
N22 Factors	S8 Triangles
N23 Division	D4 Grouped frequencies
N24 Equations	
N25 Subtraction (Red strand)	M6 Area
N25 Subtraction (Blue strand)	S9 Triangles
Recap 5 Division	
N26 Division	D5 Averages
N27 Division	D6 Probability
N28 Problem solving	
N29 Multiplication	S10 Coordinates
N30 Multiplication	M7 Area
N31 Division	
N32 Division	D7 Probability

⑤ Teaching Points

General guidance

The strategies used throughout the teacher cards reflect two basic aims:

- The development of mental strategies in solving numerical problems. These strategies are then used to produce the tactics necessary to deal with written procedures.
- The commitment of the Abacus team to helping pupils to make sense of what they are doing. The teaching, activities and textbook pages are designed to build up a series of specific techniques, strategies and skills by means of which pupils will understand and perform all the basic mathematical functions and operations.

The Abacus approach is founded upon the fact that, in order to make sense, pupils need to be provided with the following:

- **Images**, upon which to 'hang' more abstract ideas
- **Procedures** for carrying out certain operations or performing particular routines
- **Narratives** which enable them to situate what they have learned

Images

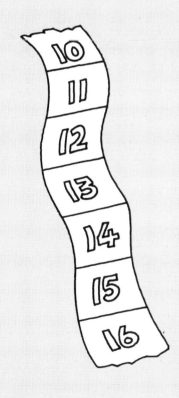

Images are powerful tools in helping pupils understand a more abstract or general idea. The Abacus Teacher Cards and the Textbook pages draw heavily upon the images of number lines and grids, money or base ten equipment, and mathematical arrays. The pupils are encouraged to visualise numbers as a line sequence, as a grid or as a rectangular arrangement of counters. For example, 24 may be envisaged as three rows of eight counters. In this way the relation between multiplication and division or sharing is illuminated. Similarly, visualising the number grid means that the pupils have something to consult, so to speak, when they need to add twenty or thirty. They can 'look' at their mental number grid.

In the same way, 'sound images' and finger movements are used to help pupils remember the number facts. Many Teacher Cards and activities require that pupils chant in unison, using their fingers to emphasise the number of twos or fives or threes counted. In this way pupils develop a kinaesthetic memory (a memory based on body movements) which then becomes a cognitive memory (a memory based on a mental picture). In this respect, the aural chant and the body movement become steps on the way to an automatic performance. The pupil knows what six fives are because, when they fold the end of their sixth finger, the number thirty is triggered in their memory. The number facts may literally become part of them!

Procedures

The Teacher Cards frequently demonstrate a way of doing something in mathematics. Pupils are shown how to subtract two numbers in their heads:

Round the first number up to its nearest ten to help you take away a multiple of ten, e.g. 45 take away 29 is the same as 46 take away 30.

Or we model division in terms of its relation to multiplication:

63 ÷ 7 asks how many sevens in sixty-three, so we use the ×7 table ...

These procedures, clearly modelled and outlined in the lesson so that they make sense to the pupils, enable them to perform the same operation as the teacher. Wherever possible, this mental procedure is related to the written algorithm. This avoids the all too common situation where pupils' mental strategies conflict with those they are asked to use when performing a written calculation. When performing a mental calculation pupils are encouraged to use such strategies as 'starting with the digits of largest value' or 'transforming a calculation to make it easier' (e.g. turning 45 – 29 into 46 – 30). These strategies are explicitly developed and practised in Abacus, with its strong focus on mental numerical tactics. Traditionally however, pupils have had to abandon these strategies as soon as they are introduced to written algorithms which require them to use tactics such as 'dealing with the units first' and 'addressing the calculation as set'. Research has demonstrated that this conflict between the comfortable mental strategies developed by pupils and the strategies demanded in order to perform new and strange written procedures is the source of many future difficulties. Abacus avoids this confusion by developing written algorithms which are based on the pupils' carefully acquired mental strategies.

The procedures utilised on the Teacher Cards and thence in the lessons are reinforced by both the imagery and the techniques used in the Textbook pages.

Narratives

Narratives are not only stories. They are ways of organising, structuring or sequencing our knowledge or information. They also provide familiar contexts which pupils have themselves experienced, within which the mathematical concepts can appear and be recognised. Both of these aspects of narratives are utilised in Abacus 6.

Narratives are utilised as ways of structuring and sequencing pupils' mathematical knowledge through the consistent emphasis on talking things through. Pupils are required to verbalise each stage of a sequence of mental strategies. Thus, they talk themselves through what to do in a manner which strongly resembles telling a story: 'first you add the hundreds and then you add the tens and see if you have any more hundreds ...' This emphasis on the oral aspects of learning

Teaching Points

mathematical procedures greatly strengthens pupils' grasp of these mental strategies.

Narratives also provide the contexts in Abacus for pupils to practise and rehearse their mathematics. Carrying luggage on a journey, working out the total length of two pieces of furniture, and calculating increased scores in a computer game, all produce situations in which the skills acquired in a more mathematical setting can be practised in the context of a broader picture.

There are a number of more general points to be made about Abacus which teachers will find helpful in managing this scheme in their classroom.

1. Structured apparatus

Abacus requires no extra or expensive structured apparatus in the classroom. The resources required are either supplied in the Resource Pack, or consist of materials that will be readily available in most classrooms, such as interlocking cubes, plastic money, base ten equipment, dice or dominoes. A full list of requirements is given in Appendix (i) on page 44.

2. A topic approach to shape, data and measurement

The approach to all areas of shape, data and measurement has been carefully planned to link with the work the pupils are covering in Number. The Teacher Cards are designed to allow maximum flexibility in terms of the teaching of shape, data and measurement, and so it is a very simple matter for any teacher adopting a topic approach to collect together the cards for any one topic, e.g. length, and to teach these as a block. The follow-up work in terms of relevant activities, Textbook pages and Photocopy Masters will be signalled as usual on the reverse of each Teacher Card.

3. Building upon Key Stage 1 mathematics

Abacus adopts a structured approach to the teaching and learning of numerical skills. Therefore the procedures and methods used throughout the Key Stage 1 materials are designed and selected specifically with the mathematical requirements of the Key Stage 2 curriculum in mind. In Key Stage 2 the pupils are encouraged, through the use of particular strategies, to build up both a mental facility with numbers and an ability to record what they are doing in a way that makes sense to themselves and others.

This structured approach is particularly evident in the development of written procedures. The pupils are always encouraged to build up mental strategies before turning to the written formulation. Thus, there is a strong emphasis on adding ten and multiples of ten, and on a good knowledge of the addition bonds, both of which facilitate mental addition.

The pupils are always required to read the number sentences, to verbalise them, so that they make sense of what they are being asked to do. Detailed attention has been paid in Abacus to the development of prerequisite skills. This means that, at each stage, the Teacher Cards will address the very specific skills necessary to get to the next levels in the procedures.

Teachers need to be able to rely upon a mathematics programme to develop each pupil's profile of skills in such a way that the 'basic' skills are on automatic pilot, by the time they are required as part of a more complex procedure. Teachers also need to be reassured that pupils acquire a numerical fluency which enables them to 'read' number problems in such a way as to make sense of them and to understand how to address them. Abacus has been developed with these requirements very specifically in mind, and this is the reason for our structured and systematic approach to the teaching of number.

Specific guidance on Abacus 6

In order to get the best out of the strategies utilised on the Abacus 6 Teacher Cards, teachers are advised to attend to the following points:

Pre-requisite skills

In Abacus R to 5 strong emphasis has been placed on the development of specific mental number skills. This enables Abacus 6 to draw upon specific mental strategies which pupils have been developing and rehearsing in previous units. These include key skills such as adding multiples of ten, rounding up and down to the nearest ten, nearest hundred, nearest thousand, doubling, halving and finding the next ten. Included in the Teacher Cards for Abacus 6 are a series of 'Recap' cards. These provide lessons – interspersed throughout the routine number work – which allow you to rehearse and recap specific number skills if

Teaching Points

you feel that it would be helpful to do so with some or all of the class. It should also be possible to help pupils improve their mental facility with numbers by utilising the Abacus 5/6 Simmering Activities book.

As pupils progress in their mathematics careers, it becomes increasingly important that they build up a bank of key skills, particularly in relation to numeracy. In Abacus, these key skills form the core of the number work, and pupils are encouraged and directed to re-visit these skills in the context of many areas of numeracy. In this way, pupils develop and practise their mental strategies, and acquire a fluency and an automaticity in their calculations which is of immense assistance as they move on to more complex procedures in Abacus 6. To support pupils' acquisition of this bank of key skills, particular teacher attention is directed to the following:

- reading, ordering and recognising place-value in large numbers (R1, N1)
- reading, ordering and recognising place-value in decimal numbers: 1 and 2 places (N2, N3)
- rounding decimal numbers (2 places) to their nearest whole number and nearest tenth (N4)
- recognising addition bonds to 10, 20, 100, 1000 (R2, N5)
- adding and subtracting involving 2-, 3- and 4-digit numbers (N6, N25)
- adding and subtracting involving decimal numbers: 1 and 2 places (R3, N10, N12)
- recognising the next whole number after a decimal number and what must be added to reach it (N11)
- adding positive and negative numbers (N7)
- recognising simple fractions, mixed fractions and equivalent fractions (R4, N16, N17)
- relating fractions, decimals and percentages (N18, N19)
- knowing multiplication facts up to 10×10 (N8)
- multiplying by 10, 100 (N13)
- multiplying 2-digit and 3-digit numbers by 1-digit numbers (N14, N15)
- multiplying 2-digit and 3-digit numbers by 2-digit numbers (N25, N26)
- multiplying decimal numbers (1 place) by 1-digit numbers (N30, N31)
- dividing as the inverse of multiplying and knowing the division facts related to the multiplication facts up to 10×10 (N9)
- dividing 2-digit and 3-digit numbers by 1-digit numbers (R5, N27)
- recognising tests for divisibility (N23)
- dividing decimal numbers (1 place) by 1-digit numbers (N30, N31)
- recognising multiples and factors of numbers (N20, N22)
- recognising squares and square roots (N21)

In addition, Abacus allows the teacher to focus upon the development of key strategies in numeracy, including:

- the ability to estimate an approximate answer
- approximating, particularly rounding to the nearest 10, 100 or 1000
- transforming a calculation to make it easier to handle
- using known number facts to obtain answers to other calculations
- relating one numerical operation to another, e.g. subtraction is the reverse of addition and division is the reverse of multiplication

Addition and subtraction

A systematic approach to addition and subtraction is adopted in Abacus. Pupils are taught, and subsequently use, prerequisite mental skills before attempting written algorithms. Thus, in addition, the pupils are taken through this structure of skills:

counting on	addition bonds to 10
adding ten	addition bonds to 20
adding a multiple of ten	looking for tens when adding several 1-digit numbers
mentally adding one 2-digit number to another	adding 9
adding two or more 2-digit numbers using a written algorithm	
adding a 2-digit number to a 3-digit number	
adding two or more 3-digit numbers	
adding two or more decimal numbers	

In subtraction, a similar structure is adopted:

counting back	recognising what must be added to get the next multiple of ten
counting back ten	finding the difference between two numbers by counting on
counting back a multiple of ten	
taking away a multiple of ten using vertical notation	
taking away one 2-digit number from another whose digits are both greater	
taking away one decimal number from another	

The subtraction in Abacus 6 is a natural development of the subtraction in Abacus 5. Again, the emphasis is on acquiring a mental facility for subtraction and using this in following a written algorithm.

Abacus is unique in offering an alternative subtraction algorithm to the standard method of decomposition. This alternative, which is a form of equal adding, is offered in the belief that pupils who use it will have greater success than has been the case with the method of decomposition. This is because the algorithm reinforces pupils' mental subtraction methods.

Teaching Points

The two alternative subtraction algorithms are introduced in Abacus 4 (for subtractions involving 2- and 3-digit numbers), developed in Abacus 5 (for subtractions involving 3-digit numbers and decimal numbers), and further developed in Abacus 6 (for subtractions involving decimal numbers with 2 places). Subtractions involving whole numbers with several digits are also revised in Abacus 6 (N25).

For subtractions involving numbers in which an adjustment is necessary (e.g. 358–199, 2·17–1·89), the teacher has a choice of two Teacher Cards, one for each subtraction algorithm:

N12/25 (Red strand)   method of equal adding

N12/25 (Blue strand)   method of decomposition

There is one specific Textbook page for each strand, followed by other Textbook pages which are appropriate for either method.

One unit develops the skill of recognising the next whole number after a decimal number (N11), as well as what must be added to make the next whole number. This Unit develops valuable mental skills, but also offers good preparation for pupils who use the Red strand (equal adding).

Teachers of pupils who are using Abacus for the first time with Abacus 6 will need to make decisions about which strand to follow based on the pupils' previous learning experiences in subtraction, and their level of attainment. For example, it is possible that some pupils, previously introduced to the method of decomposition, are experiencing difficulties with this method. They may well benefit from learning the method of equal adding.

Also, teachers of pupils who have used Abacus 4 and Abacus 5, need to ensure continuity of method.

The authors of Abacus have given considerable thought to how to produce confident 'subtractors' – pupils who can move comfortably between a written and a mental procedure when subtracting. We have taken seriously the evidence that a significant proportion of pupils do not succeed when learning how to subtract using decomposition. It is our belief that the alternative procedure (Red strand) is a preferable method for teachers to use.

Multiplication and division

Abacus 4 builds on the solid foundation established in Abacus 3, emphasising pattern within the multiplication tables, and links between one multiplication table and another. In Abacus 4, the ×3 and ×4 tables are consolidated, and the remaining tables introduced. The pattern in the ×9 table is emphasised, and the ×6 and ×8 tables are correspondingly linked to the ×3 and ×4 tables.

Abacus 5 builds on these experiences, leading the pupils towards immediate recall of their multiplication facts up to 10 × 10. These are further practised in Abacus 6 (N8)

In Abacus 5, the terms 'multiple', 'factor', and 'prime number' are introduced. Abacus 6 further develops these concepts (N20, N21), as well as square numbers, leading to the concept of square roots (N21).

Similarly, the development of pupils' division skills in Abacus 5 follows the principles established in Abacus 4, of linking these to the multiplication facts, so that $12 \div 4$ is read as 'twelve divided by four', interpreted as 'how many fours make twelve', and linked to 'three fours are twelve'. This is further consolidated in Abacus 6 (N9).

It is intended that as pupils develop security in their recall of multiplication facts, a corresponding security in their recall of division facts will also develop.

Abacus 5 builds on the knowledge of these multiplication facts and division facts, together with the multiplication of numbers by 10 and 100 to provide the basis for the development towards the multiplication of a 2-digit number by a 1-digit number and division of a 2-digit number by a 1-digit number.

Abacus 6 consolidates and extends these multiplication skills to include multiplying a 3-digit number by a 1-digit number (N14, N15), and multiplying 2- and 3-digit numbers by 2-digit numbers (N25, N26). Similarly, the division skills are extended to include dividing a 3-digit number by a 1-digit number (N27).

Abacus 6 also extends these multiplication and division skills to include decimal numbers (N30, N31, N32, N33).

Fractions and decimals

Fractions and decimals are approached in a systematic fashion both as parts of a whole and also as positions on a number line.

Fractions are described firstly as equal parts of a whole. They are related to images from everyday life such as bars of chocolate or cakes. The connections between simple equivalent fractions are largely made by reference to these images, e.g. half a cake is the same as two quarters. However, the pupil's understanding is then extended through a consideration of fractions of quantities. They are required to calculate fractions of small quantities, and to find both simple and multiple fractions of amounts, e.g. four fifths of 20. This work is directly related to work on doubling and halving and to their knowledge of table facts and division. Thus, the pupils are shown how to find one quarter by halving one half, and one eighth as half of one quarter. Most importantly, pupils are encouraged to see the different fractions in relation to each other, so that they recognise one eighth as related to one half, and can order fractions in terms of size.

Decimals are also introduced to pupils as equal parts of a whole (i.e. as tenths). However, this image is immediately related to their position on a number line through the tactic of a decimal strip, divided into ten parts. Thus, pupils come to envisage decimals as equal divisions along a line of numbers, and are able to make an immediate connection between decimals and the numbers they have already worked with. This helps to prevent the separation of decimals and other numbers which is behind so many pupils' (and adults') confusion, and even fear, of this subject. Through the Abacus approach, pupils come to understand decimals as positions on the number line which make sense, and can be used, in exactly the same way as other numbers.

Number lines

The image of the number line continues to be important throughout Abacus 6. The use of the number line forms a crucial part of the imagery underlying the strategies in relation to the following skills:

- rounding whole numbers to the nearest ten, hundred or thousand
- rounding decimal numbers to the nearest whole number
- subtraction as the difference between two numbers
- performing subtractions by adding to the next ten or hundred
- recognising and ordering decimal numbers
- counting and ordering large numbers

The use of a number line as an explanatory and an operational tool often enables pupils to develop the appropriate mental models to make them confident in performing mental procedures. Pupils use the number line to help them make sense of their mathematics and also to help them perform the necessary calculations. Abacus therefore utilises a number line whenever it is appropriate, and it is strongly recommended that a 100-division number line is displayed in the classroom, enabling different number cards to be placed to label the ends of the line.

Money

Money continues to provide an important context within which pupils can locate many of the mathematical operations and calculations they are performing. Money is important to pupils – and adults – in their lives outside the classroom, and therefore it is extremely helpful, both in terms of motivation and utility, to relate what the pupils are doing numerically to aspects of everyday life concerned with money. For example, subtraction and addition can be related to price reductions and increases, and multiplication and division to repeated costs and the partitioning of amounts. Where possible, Abacus draws upon plausible situations and contexts which the pupils could encounter in their life outside school, and relates these to the numerical demands of the topic being taught.

Measures

In all aspects of measures (e.g. length, weight, capacity, area, angle, etc.), Abacus provides pupils with activities that develop the important skills of estimation. These skills enhance pupils' understanding of the measurement concepts involved.

Abacus 6 links both Imperial and metric units of measurement, and gives pupils the opportunity to make approximate conversions from one to the other.

Area

In Abacus 4 pupils are led to recognise that the area of a rectangle can be calculated by multiplying length × width. This is further consolidated in Abacus 5. This is consistent with the way in which the concept of multiplication is developed using rows and columns of arrays. Pupils continue to use the square centimetre as a measure alongside cm^2 notation. The calculation of the area of a right-angled triangle is introduced as one half of the rectangle of which it is part.

Abacus 6 extends this idea to calculate the area of any triangle given its length of base and height, by splitting it into two right-angled triangles.

Capacity and volume

In Abacus 3 and 4, volume and capacity are introduced and developed separately. Volume, which is the amount of space used by a 3-d object, is introduced by counting cubes in model cuboids. Capacity, on the other hand, is a measure of the amount a container can hold. Abacus 3 leads pupils from measuring capacities in terms of 'more than' or 'less than' a litre, towards using a litre measure, and more accurate measures of capacity in units of 100 ml.

In Abacus 4 pupils are introduced to measuring capacity in centilitres, and are encouraged to begin to appreciate the relationships between the different standard units: litre, centilitre, millilitre. The measuring of volumes of cuboids includes the introduction of the cubic centimetre and cm^3 notation.

Abacus 5 brings the concepts of volume and capacity together, using cubic centimetres for the volume of an open cuboid, and litres for its capacity. Links between the two units are then made. The use of cm^3 notation is required.

Abacus 6 links both Imperial and metric units of measurement, and gives pupils the opportunity to make approximate conversions from one to the other.

Weight and mass

Throughout this stage of work in Abacus the word 'weight' is used in preference to 'mass'. Scientifically, the weight of an object is the force exerted by the Earth's gravitational field on an object: weight can then be crudely interpreted as the pull towards the ground. The mass of an object is the quantity of matter it contains. The force of attraction varies with the position of the object, but the quantity of matter remains fixed. The weight of an object can be found by using a spring balance, bathroom scale or direct-reading kitchen scale, but the mass has to be found by using balance scales where an object is placed

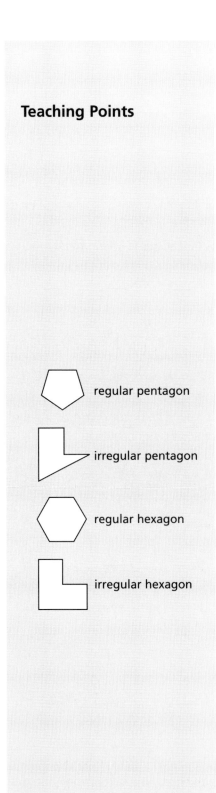

regular pentagon

irregular pentagon

regular hexagon

irregular hexagon

in one pan and a balance obtained by placing objects of known mass in the other.

Though this distinction between weight and mass is clear to the scientist, it is rarely made in daily life. As pupils progress through Abacus this distinction will be relatively easy to grasp but at this stage the word weight is used in accordance with its everyday usage. If you are concerned about this decision, the word mass may be used when it is obviously more appropriate, but the intention is that no undue worry should be centred around the distinction between the two words. Many of the Number Units use contexts involving weight to develop skills in number. These contexts are included both to relate the work in number to pupils' everyday experiences, as well as to develop the concepts in weight which have been introduced in earlier Abacus years.

Regular and irregular 2-d shapes

A pentagon is a five-sided polygon (a 2-d shape with straight sides). Pentagons can be regular (all sides are the same length, and all angles the same size), or irregular (all sides are not the same length, nor angles the same size). Pentagons in packs of shapes tend to be regular. It is not necessary, at this stage, for pupils to distinguish between the two types, but it is important for them to see both regular and irregular pentagons, and recognise all five-sided polygons as pentagons. The same is true of hexagons, octagons etc. Consequently, the Teacher Cards and Textbook pages include both regular and irregular polygons.

Parallel, perpendicular, vertical, horizontal

These terms are introduced in Abacus 5. Parallel and perpendicular are introduced first. Parallel lines are defined as *straight* lines which never meet, no matter how far they are extended; and perpendicular lines as lines which meet at right-angles. This builds on the concept of a right-angle developed in previous Abacus years.

The definitions of horizontal and vertical are then developed from the concepts of parallel and perpendicular. Horizontal is parallel to the horizon, and vertical is perpendicular to the horizon.

On a sheet of paper, horizontal lines are interpreted as 'across from left to right' and vertical lines as 'from top to bottom'. Whilst it is understood that any straight line drawn on a page and placed flat on the table is in a 'horizontal' plane, and therefore horizontal, it is felt best to avoid this concept at this stage.

The concept of horizontal and vertical can be further developed with reference to axes in the work on coordinates (S10).

Circles

In Abacus 4 pupils are introduced to the terms 'diameter' and 'radius', and participate in activities which involve measuring these for

triangular prism

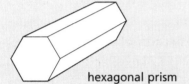

hexagonal prism

different circles. It should be noted that the diameter and radius are distances or lengths on a circle. 'Circumference', which is another length on a circle is introduced in Abacus 5.

Pupils are introduced to the approximate relationship between diameter and circumference, i.e. that the circumference is approximately three times the diameter of *any* circle (S3).

The term 'arc' is introduced in Abacus 6, leading to the approximate calculation of the length of an arc for semi- and quarter-circles, given the radius or diameter.

Prisms

A prism is a 3-d shape whose cross-section is always the same shape. Consequently, the two end-pieces are this same shape. If the shape of the end-piece is a triangle, the prism is called a triangular prism. If it is a pentagon, then it is called a pentagonal prism etc.
If the end-piece is a square or rectangle, then the prism might be a cube or a cuboid. So cubes and cuboids are special types of prism.
The concept of 'cross-section' is a difficult one for pupils at this stage. Since many packs of cheese are prism-shapes, the idea of the same shaped cross-section can be illustrated by slicing though packs of cheese.

Faces, edges, sides, corners, vertices

Although the correct mathematical name for the 'corner' of 2-d and 3-d shapes is vertex (plural vertices), Abacus uses the more easily recognised word 'corner' in Abacus 3, and introduces the word 'vertex' in Abacus 4. The correct terminology is 'sides' and 'vertices' for 2-d shapes, and 'edges', 'faces' and 'vertices' for 3-d shapes.

Abacus 6 introduces the concept of parallel and perpendicular faces (S3).

Angle

There are two introductory concepts of angle, both of which are considered in Abacus 3. The first is the 'static' concept, where the angle is one joining two straight lines – the edges of a book, for example. The second is the 'dynamic' concept, where the angle is a measure of turn, e.g. the angle turned by the minute hand of a clock.

In Abacus 4 the turning aspect is developed by relating angle to the eight-point compass directions.

Abacus 5 introduces degree measure and relates this measure to right-angles. The protractor is introduced as an instrument for both measuring and drawing angles in degrees. Most pupils find a protractor a difficult instrument to master. It is often helpful to encourage pupils to measure one angle using both scales to develop confidence in using the protractor.

The terms 'acute', 'obtuse' and 'reflex' angles are introduced in Abacus 6 (S5), leading to the classification of triangles into 'acute-angled', 'obtuse-angled' and 'right-angled' (S7). In Unit S6, angles are calculated on a line and at a point, given the other angles in each case. Unit S8 introduces the angle sum of a triangle, and the calculation of one angle given the other two. This is then developed to further classify triangles into 'isosceles', 'equilateral' and 'scalene' (S9).

Symmetry

Line symmetry is introduced and developed in Abacus 3 and 4. In Abacus 5, this concept is developed further towards recognising a line of symmetry, locating a line of symmetry, constructing a shape or pattern which is symmetrical in a given line (S6).

Abacus 5 introduces the concept of rotational symmetry. In addition to a Unit specifically on rotation in Abacus 4, we have developed ideas associated with rotation throughout the scheme, through the use of hands of a clock, compass directions etc.

Rotational symmetry occurs when a shape or object is rotated about a fixed point through one complete revolution, and it 'matches its image' or 'returns to its starting position' more than once in doing so. *Any* object will match its image at least once, i.e. when it returns to its starting position. Only an object which matches its image more than once is said to have rotational symmetry. The number of times it matches its image in one complete revolution is defined as its order of rotational symmetry. This is introduced in Abacus 6.

Position

Position on a grid can be located in two different ways, and it is important to distinguish between them. If the horizontal and vertical lines of the grid are labelled, then positions are located by the point where two lines meet. If the spaces between the grid lines are labelled, then positions are located by the grid cell where the two spaces meet. In Abacus 3 we focus on locating position by labelling the spaces. In Abacus 4, the idea of locating position is extended to identifying points (coordinates). This is consolidated in Abacus 5 (S10).

In Abacus 6, the coordinate axes are extended to include four quadrants, leading to negative coordinates.

Graphs

Abacus requires that all graphs are titled and have labelled axes. Usually, the horizontal axis represents the item (e.g. types of sport), and the vertical axis represents the frequency (e.g. number of votes).

In a block graph (introduced in Abacus 1 and 2), the numbering of the frequencies on the vertical axis should be written in the spaces between the blocks.

A bar graph (introduced in Abacus 3) is similar to a block graph, but uses a bar to replace each tower of blocks. In a bar graph, the numbering on the vertical axis should be written directly alongside the divisions. Also, items on the horizontal axis, should be separated, to leave spaces between the bars. In Abacus 4, bar graphs are extended to include those with vertical scales graded in units of 2, 5, etc. Bar-line graphs are introduced in Abacus 5 (D1). These are similar to bar graphs, except that the bar is replaced by a line. In the Resource Pack Photocopy Masters, there is a blank bar-line graph, on which pupils can draw their graphs accurately.

Abacus 6 introduces the line graph (D2), which includes conversion graphs for converting from one unit of measurement to another (D3). Pie charts are also introduced in Abacus 6 (D1).

Averages

There are several different types of average. The most commonly used is the **mean**, which is introduced in Abacus 5, and further developed in Abacus 6. This is the average obtained by finding the total of the observations and dividing by the number of them. Two further averages are introduced: the **mode** (the most frequently occurring observation) and the **median** (the middle observation when they are arranged in ascending sequence). If there are an even number of observations, then two middle numbers exist. The median, in this case, is the mean of these two middle numbers.

Probability

The concept of chance was introduced in Abacus 3, and developed in Abacus 4. There is no need to mention the word 'probability' at this stage. The main objective is to lay the foundation for introducing pupils to the idea that events can have different 'chances' of happening. In Abacus 3 events are classified as 'impossible', 'uncertain' or 'certain'. This classification is gradually extended in Abacus 4 to embrace 'impossible', 'unlikely', 'likely' and 'certain'.

In Abacus 4 the pupils are introduced to dice throwing experiments in which the events are equally likely. They are encouraged to predict the frequency of throws before collecting the data with a view to beginning to appreciate the equally-likely aspect of the events. This also involves intuitive ideas of division and average.

Abacus 5 consolidates these ideas as well as extending them to include events which are not equally likely (D5). Unit D4 gives the pupils experience in listing all the possible outcomes of an event, which forms the basis for future understanding of the concept of probability.

Abacus 6 introduces the term 'probability' together with the probability scale 0 to 1, and begins to assign probabilities to events.

6 Introducing Abacus to your school

As a new programme, Abacus may be introduced to a whole school at once, or it may be started with a class of pupils who have come from other schools, and who have not previously been working with the Abacus approach. This section will help teachers start Abacus in their classes, where it is new to the pupils.

Abacus is not based on an individualised approach to the learning of mathematics. Therefore, there are particular key skills that are developed with and taught to the class as a whole, using the strategies outlined on the Teacher Cards, and in the Simmering Activities. This means that pupils who have not previously used Abacus may not have acquired the same mental facility of similarly aged pupils exposed to Abacus, with its stress on these key mental skills. Since each stage of Abacus builds upon, and to some extent assumes, this mental fluency, we suggest that teachers adopt the following strategies when introducing Abacus to a new class.

Key skills

It is essential to build up key mental mathematical skills so that pupils can deal with the content of the Abacus 6 Teacher Cards. There are two ways of helping pupils acquire these key skills. Firstly, allow for a short mental maths session every day, during which you focus on particular skills using some of the ideas mentioned below. Secondly, begin the term by spending three or four weeks rehearsing some basic number work using some Abacus 5 Teacher Cards, and sections of the Abacus 6 Numeracy Support Book. The following will be particularly helpful:

Abacus 5 Teacher Cards N2, R2, N3, N4, N6, N11, N15, N25, N29
Abacus 6 Numeracy Support Book Sections 1, 2, 3, 6, 7, 8, 9

These Teacher Cards and the Numeracy Support Book will provide the images and the vocabulary to help you reinforce key skills. It should be possible to work through two to three Teacher Cards in a week.

Rehearsing mental maths skills

Every day, focus for 10 to 15 minutes on mental maths.
Each session, rehearse a particular skill, e.g. adding multiples of 10 and near multiples of 10. Demonstrate the strategy first, using a visual image if possible (e.g. a number grid). Then allow for plenty of individual and group practice.
The following techniques can be particularly helpful:
- **Grids** Draw a grid on the board, and write a number in each space. The pupils perform a particular operation on each number (e.g. adding 100), trying to keep up with you as you write the numbers.

- **Quiz** Prepare a list of 20 questions, all involving the same skill. Pupils work in pairs or alone and answer all 20 questions. Set a time limit. Can they improve on yesterday's score?
- **True or false** Write a list of number sentences on the board, focusing on one skill. The pupils have to decide if each statement is true or false.
- **Memorising and chanting** Help pupils to memorise skills by chanting them altogether. Use a 'look, cover, write, check' system, where you write a 'fact' on the board (e.g. 35 + 65 = 100), the pupils look at it, then you cover it, and the class say it. Repeat for a series of similar facts.

Key Skills for Abacus 6

Key skills	Examples
Secure knowledge of numbers to 1000	Write 'six hundred and three' in figures. Know the value of '4' in 247.
Rounding 2- and 3-digit numbers to nearest ten and hundred Rounding decimals (tenths) to nearest whole number	352 → 350 487 → 500 2.3 → 2
Understanding of decimals to one place	Know that 0.2 = 2/10 Order 3.4, 4.3, and 3.1
Rapid recall of addition bonds to 10 Adding to make the next ten and the next hundred	1 and 9, 2 and 8, 3 and 7, ... 24 + 6 = 30, 89 + 1 = 90 234 + 66 = 300, 541 + 59 = 600
Adding three or four 1-digit numbers	2 + 5 + 8 + 4 (add the 2 and 8 first) 4 + 9 + 3 (add 9 by adding 10 and taking one away)
Subtracting by counting on or counting back	23 − 4 = 19 (count back from 23) 32 − 29 = 3 (counting on from 29)
Adding multiples of ten or a hundred	48 + 40, 36 + 50 239 + 300, 421 + 500
Multiplying by ten or a multiple of ten	2 × 10, 13 × 10, 45 × 10 10 × 20, 14 × 20, 32 × 30
Rapid recall of most multiplication tables	×2, ×5, ×10, ×3, ×4, ×9, square numbers
Dividing with remainders	23 ÷ 4, 47 ÷ 5

7 Appendices

Appendix (i): List of Materials

Materials provided in Resource Pack

Number cards (0 to 10):	(10 sets)
Place-value cards	
Units (1 to 9)	(2 sets)
Tens (10 to 90)	(2 sets)
Hundreds (100 to 900)	(2 sets)
Thousands (1000 to 9000)	(2 sets)
Large number grid (1 to 100)	(1 large grid)
Card windows	(set of 6)
Resource Pack Photocopy masters	Duplicates of all the cards, along with extra resources
Group Activity Photocopy Masters	Photocopiable group activities, related to the Teacher Cards

Assumed mathematical materials in classroom

Interlocking cubes
Centimetre cubes
Counters
Spotty dice (1 to 6), numbered dice (1 to 6)
Ten-sided dice
Blank dice (can be numbered for particular activities)
Calculators
Dominoes
Playing cards
Coins
Sets of plastic 2-d shapes
Sets of solid 3-d shapes
Metre sticks (calibrated in dm, and in cm)
30 cm rulers
Containers (for Capacity)
Analogue clock with movable hands
Digital clock
Stop-clock
Weighing balances
1 kg and 100 g weights
Base ten equipment
3-d model-making material (e.g. Polydron, Clixi)
Geoboards
Direction compass

Other materials

Cloth bags
Blu-Tack
Post-it Notes

Appendix (ii): Abacus 6 Record of Work

This record keeping grid allows you to record which units have been attempted by the whole class or by individual groups (1, 2, 3, 4, 5, 6).

UNIT	GROUPS						
	Whole Class	1	2	3	4	5	6
R1 Number To recognise place-value of digits in 3- or 4-digit numbers							
N1 Number To recognise numbers as large as one million or more To rehearse the place-value of digits in large numbers							
N2 Decimals To rehearse recognition of decimal notation (one place) To rehearse ordering decimal numbers (one place)							
N3 Decimals To rehearse decimal notation (2 places) To locate the position of decimal numbers on a number line							
N4 Decimals To round decimal numbers (2 places) to their nearest whole number and nearest tenth							
R2 Addition To recognise and learn addition bonds to 10 To recognise pairs of multiples of 10 which make 100							
N5 Addition To recognise and learn addition bonds to 100 To recognise and learn addition bonds to 1000							
N6 Addition To add two or more numbers, including numbers with different numbers of digits To estimate the results of these additions							
N7 Number To rehearse the position of negative numbers on the number line To add positive and negative numbers							
N8 Multiplication To rehearse and consolidate the recognition of multiplication facts up to 10×10							
N9 Division To rehearse and consolidate the recognition of division facts related to multiplication facts							
R3 Addition To add two decimal numbers (1 place), without carrying							
N10 Addition To add two decimal number (1 place), with carrying To add two decimal numbers (2 places) with carrying							
N11 Addition To recognise the next whole number after a decimal number (2 places) To recognise what must be added to a decimal number (2 places) to make the next whole number							
N12 Subtraction (Red strand) To subtract one decimal number (2 places) from another with equal adding							
N12 Subtraction (Blue strand) To subtract one decimal number (2 places) from another with decomposition							
N13 Multiplication To multiply by 10 or 100 To multiply by multiples of 10 or 100							
N14 Multiplication To multiply a 2-digit number by a 1-digit number							
N15 Multiplication To multiply a 2-digit number by a 2-digit number							
R4 Fractions To rehearse the notion of simple fractions							

Abacus 6 Record of Work

UNIT	Whole Class	GROUPS					
		1	2	3	4	5	6
N16 Fractions To recognise mixed fractions							
N17 Fractions To rehearse recognition of equivalent fractions To convert fractions to their simplest form							
N18 Percentages To rehearse recognition of percentages To relate fractions, decimals and percentages							
N19 Percentages To find a percentage of a quantity To recognise everyday uses of percentages							
N20 Multiples To understand the term 'multiple' To list the multiples of a number To recognise multiples common to two or more numbers							
N21 Square numbers To rehearse the meaning of square numbers To introduce the concept of the square root of a number							
N22 Factors To rehearse the meaning of 'factor' To list the factors of a number To recognise prime numbers							
N23 Division To recognise numbers which divide by 2, 3, 4, 5, 6 and 10							
N24 Equations To introduce the concept of letters to represent unknown numbers in simple equations To solve simple equations by substitution							
N25 Subtraction (Red strand) To subtract one whole number from another (with equal adding)							
N25 Subtraction (Blue strand) To subtract one whole number from another (with decomposition)							
R5 Division To rehearse dividing a 2-digit number by a 1-digit number							
N26 Division To divide a 3-digit by a 1-digit number, with remainders							
N27 Division To divide a 3-digit number by a 2-digit multiple of 10							
N28 Problem solving To solve problems involving different operations							
N29 Multiplication To multiply a decimal number (1 and 2 places) by 10, 100							
N30 Multiplication To multiply a decimal number (1 place) by a 1-digit number							
N31 Division To divide a whole number by 10 and by 100							
N32 Division To divide a decimal number (1 place) by a 1-digit number							
M1 Length To introduce the kilometre as a measure To rehearse the relationship between kilometres and metres To introduce the relationship between kilometres and miles							
M2 Speed To introduce the concept of speed and its relationship with distance and time							
M3 Volume and capacity To consolidate the relationship between different units of volume and capacity							
M4 Capacity To link metric and imperial units of capacity							
M5 Weight To link metric and imperial units of weight							

Abacus 6 Record of Work

UNIT	Whole Class	1	2	3	4	5	6
M6 Area To calculate area by dissecting To find the area of a triangle							
M7 Area To find the area of a circle							
S1 2-d shape To rehearse the names of common 2-d shapes (including parallelogram and rhombus) To introduce 'trapezium' To introduce 'quadrilateral'							
S2 2-d shape To rehearse the names of distances on a circle To rehearse the approximate relationship between diameter and circumference To introduce the 'arc' of a circle							
S3 3-d shape To rehearse the names of common 3-d shapes To recognise parallel and perpendicular faces							
S4 Symmetry To rehearse the recognition of line symmetry To rehearse the recognition of rotational symmetry To introduce the 'order' of rotational symmetry							
S5 Angle To introduce acute, obtuse and reflex angles To recognise acute, obtuse and reflex angles in shapes							
S6 Angle To calculate angles on straight line, or at a point							
S7 Triangles To introduce acute-angles, and obtuse-angled triangles To sort triangles according to type							
S8 Triangles To explore the angle sum of a triangle To calculate one angle of a triangle, given the other two							
S9 Triangles To introduce names of triangles: isosceles, equilateral, scalene							
S10 Coordinates To rehearse reading and plotting points in the first quadrant of a coordinate grid To extend the coordinate grid to four quadrants							
D1 Pie charts To introduce a pie chart to represent data To construct and interpret a pie chart							
D2 Line graphs To introduce a line graph To construct and interpret a line graph							
D3 Conversion graphs To construct and interpret a conversion graph							
D4 Grouped frequencies To group continuous data in equal intervals To construct a grouped frequency table To draw and interpret a graph (histogram) based on equal intervals							
D5 Averages To rehearse the concept of average To rehearse the calculation of the mean To introduce the median and mode							
D6 Probability To introduce the probability scale 0 to 1 To assign probabilities to events							
D7 Probability To list all the outcomes of an event To assign probabilities to an event							

I can...

use simple fractions & percentages to describe proportions of a whole.
4N14, 15   5N23, 27   6N16, 17

Appendix (iii): Assessment Grid (Key Stage 2)

To assist with statutory assessment, selected items from the level descriptions are included within the Assessment Grid. For each item, key stages within the scheme are identified. This gives you a quick reference for reporting progress.

You can then quickly assess achievement using an on/off principle. The pupil **can do** or **cannot do**. There are no interim stages on the records.

- The system allows a cumulative record to develop.
- Each box can be completed in a variety of ways:
  - a simple tick or colouring in by you or pupil
  - a colouring in using a different colour for each year: red for Reception, green for Year 1, pink for Year 2, ... blue for Year 6.
  - or preferably a half-termly code from Reception to Year 6 as follows.

There are seven primary years included in Abacus from Reception (R) to Year 6 (Y6): R, Y1, Y2, Y3, Y4, Y5, Y6. There are six half terms in each academic year coded from 1 to 6: 1, 2, 3, 4, 5, 6.

The code is as follows, if a pupil satisfies a particular statement of attainment in the first half term of their reception year it is labelled R–1 in the appropriate box of the grid in use. Similarly a statement satisfied in the last half term of Year 5 would be labelled Y5–6.

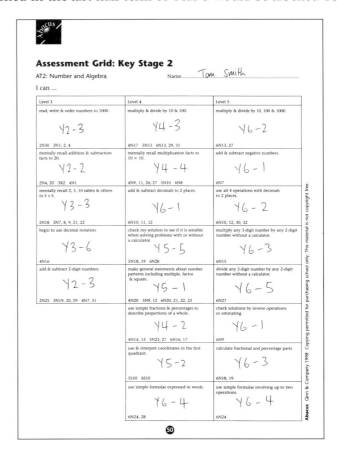

Primary Year Groups	Academic year					
	Autumn Term		Spring Term		Summer Term	
	1	2	3	4	5	6
Reception	R–1	R–2	R–3	R–4	R–5	R–6
Year 1	Y1–1	Y1–2	Y1–3	Y1–4	Y1–5	Y1–6
Year 2	Y2–1	Y2–2	Y2–3	Y2–4	Y2–5	Y2–6
Year 3	Y3–1	Y3–2	Y3–3	Y3–4	Y3–5	Y3–6
Year 4	Y4–1	Y4–2	Y4–3	Y4–4	Y4–5	Y4–6
Year 5	Y5–1	Y5–2	Y5–3	Y5–4	Y5–5	Y5–6
Year 6	Y6–1	Y6–2	Y6–3	Y6–4	Y6–5	Y6–6

At the bottom of each box is a code showing where to check this particular statement (of the form 4N14 – Abacus 4, Unit N14 or 5N23, 27 – Abacus 5, Units N23, N27). In some instances this will be at different stages within the scheme to match the development of individual pupils.

The indications at this stage are in phase with the overall Abacus progression from Abacus R to Abacus 6. Consequently, only references up to the end of Abacus 5 are included in the grids. The assessment grids develop in phase with the natural progression within Abacus.

There is space in each box for you to record a short comment if appropriate. The record sheets can also be used as:
- a prompt at the planning stage
- part of a record of achievement
- a tool for feeding back to parents
- a check of a pupil's individual progress
- an assessment of group or whole class progress.

The items included within the assessment grid are taken from the programme of study and appropriate level descriptions of each attainment target in the National Curriculum.

You will be able to use the cumulative information contained within the grid, together with your global view of the pupil's progress and any other factors you think appropriate, in coming to a decision about whether the pupil has successfully achieved the appropriate level within each attainment target.

There is no suggestion that the grid alone will provide the only evidence for making end of year or end of key stage assessments. Abacus is in full accord with the objectives in the National Curriculum in wanting these decisions to be based on the level description as a whole rather than simply a collection of disparate items.

Assessment Grid: Key Stage 2

AT1: Using and Applying Mathematics   Name...

I can ...

Level 3	Level 4	Level 5
find ways of overcoming difficulties when solving problems.	develop my own strategies for solving problems.	carry through a task by identifying & obtaining information, checking results & considering if these are sensible.
use or interpret accurately maths terms and maths aspects in everyday language.	present information & results in a clear, organised way & give explanations.	describe situations in a variety of mathematical forms.
investigate general statements by trying out some examples.	search for a pattern to try out ideas of my own.	make a generalisation, test it & explain my reasoning.

Abacus Ginn & Company 1998 Copying permitted for purchasing school only. This material is not copyright free.

Assessment Grid: Key Stage 2

AT2: Number and Algebra

Name...

I can ...

Level 3	Level 4	Level 5
read, write & order numbers to 1000. 2N30 3N1, 2, 4	multiply & divide by 10 & 100. 4N17 5N13 6N13, 29, 31	multiply & divide by 10, 100 & 1000. 6N13, 27
mentally recall addition & subtraction facts to 20. 2N4, 20 3R2 4N1	mentally recall multiplication facts to 10 × 10. 4N9, 11, 26, 27 5N10 6N8	add & subtract negative numbers. 6N7
mentally recall 2, 5, 10 tables & others to 5 × 5. 2N18 3N7, 8, 9, 21, 22	add & subtract decimals to 2 places. 6N10, 11, 12	use all 4 operations with decimals to 2 places. 6N10, 12, 30, 32
begin to use decimal notation. 4N16	check my solution to see if it is sensible when solving problems with or without a calculator. 5N18, 19 6N28	multiply any 3-digit number by any 2-digit number without a calculator. 6N15
add & subtract 2-digit numbers. 2N25 3N19, 20, 29 4N7, 31	make general statements about number patterns including multiple, factor & square. 4N20 5N9, 12 6N20, 21, 22, 23	divide any 3-digit number by any 2-digit number without a calculator. 6N27
	use simple fractions & percentages to describe proportions of a whole. 4N14, 15 5N23, 27 6N16, 17	check solutions by inverse operations or estimating. 6N9
	use & interpret coordinates in the first quadrant. 5S10 6S10	calculate fractional and percentage parts. 6N18, 19
	use simple formulae expressed in words. 6N24, 28	use simple formulae involving up to two operations. 6N24

Assessment Grid: Key Stage 2

AT3: Shape, Space & Measures   Name...

I can ...

Level 3	Level 4	Level 5
sort 2-d & 3-d shapes using mathematical properties. 2S1, 3 3S1, 4 4S2	construct simple 3-d models & draw 2-d shapes & know associated language. 4S3, 4 5S2, 3, 4	measure & draw accurately when constructing 3-d models. 6S3
recognise reflective symmetry. 2S5 3S5	recognise rotational symmetry. 5S6 6S4	identify all the symmetries of plane shapes. 6S1, 4
estimate using units of measurement. 2M4,5,7 3M2, 5, 7	reflect simple shapes in a mirror line. 5S5	measure angle to the nearest degree. 5S9 6S5, 6, 7, 8
use standard units – cm, dm, m, g, kg, l, s, min, ml, etc. 2M4, 5, 6, 9 3M2, 5, 7 4M1, 2, 4, 5, 7	choose & use appropriate units & instruments for measurement. 4M4, 5, 10 5M2, 3 6M1, 3	make sensible estimates for measures in everyday situations. 6M1, 2, 3, 4, 5
use simple measuring instruments accurately. 2M5,8,9 3M2,5,7 4M7	find perimeters of simple shapes, areas by counting squares & volumes by counting cubes. 4M3, 6 5M4, 5 6M3, 6 6S2	make rough metric conversions for Imperial units still in use. 6M1, 4, 5

Assessment Grid: Key Stage 2

AT4: Handling Data   Name...

I can ...

Level 1	Level 2
sort objects describing criteria used. RS1–4	sort objects using more than one criterion. 2N12, 21
	record results in simple tables, block graphs & diagrams. 2N22 3D1

Level 3	Level 4	Level 5
interpret data from simple tables and lists. 3D3 4D1, 3 4M8, 9	construct a frequency table. 4D1 5D3	understand & use the mean. 5D2 6D5
construct & interpret bar charts & pictograms. 3D2 4D2 5D1	use the mode & median of a set of data. 6D5	compare 2 simple distributions using range & a measure of average. 6D5
	represent & interpret data in a frequency diagram. 4D1 5D3 6D4	interpret statistical diagrams such as pie chart, conversion graph. 6D1, 3
	construct & interpret simple line graphs. 6D2	understand & use the probability scale. 6D6
	understand & use simple probability words such as fair, certain, likely. 3D4 4D4, 5 5D4, 5	estimate & justify the probability of an event. 6D7

Appendix (iv): Unit sequence (Key Stage 2)

Abacus 3	Abacus 4	Abacus 5	Abacus 6

References are to Teacher Cards within each year. AT1 of the National Curriculum and the use of calculators are an integral part of the course.

General number

Abacus 3	Abacus 4	Abacus 5	Abacus 6
Recognise, count, write, order numbers to 100 R1	Recognise, count, write order numbers to 1000 R4	Recognise, count, write, order numbers to 1000 R1	Recognise, count, write, order numbers to 1000 R1
Recognise, count, write numbers to 1000 N1, N2, N4, R8	Recognise, count, write, order numbers to 10 000 N18	Recognise, count, write order numbers to 10 000 N1	Recognise, count, write, order numbers to 100 000 N1
Pattern – odd, even N16	Pattern – odd, even N20	Pattern – square numbers N28	Recognise, write, order decimal numbers N3
Addition patterns N17			
Pattern in number sequences N27	Rounding to nearest 10, 100 N19, N23, N29	Rounding to the nearest 10, 100, 1000 N2, N6, N18	Pattern - squares and roots N21
		Rounding decimals to the nearest whole number N16, N20	Rounding decimals to the nearest whole number and nearest tenth N4, N11
		Negative numbers N14	Negative numbers and addition N7
		Multiples and factors N9, N12	Multiples, factors and primes N20, N22
			Equations N24

Operations with number

Addition

Abacus 3	Abacus 4	Abacus 5	Abacus 6
Addition to 20 R2, N3, N5	Addition to 20 N1	Addition to 100 R2, N3	Addition to 1000 R2, N5, N6
Add several 1-digit numbers N6	Add multiples of 10 R2	Add multiples of 10 N4	
Addition to 100 N11, N12, R5, R7	Add 2-digit numbers N6, N7	Add 4-digit numbers N19	
Add 2-digit numbers N18, N19, N20	Add 3-digit numbers N21, N22	Add tenths (decimals) N17	Adding tenths and hundredths N3, N11
	Addition bonds to 100 N28		

Subtraction

Abacus 3	Abacus 4	Abacus 5	Abacus 6
Subtraction to 100 N10, N13, R4, N14, N15	Subtraction to 100 N2, N3, N23	Subtraction to 100 R3	
Subtraction 2-digit numbers N28, N29	Subtraction 2-digit numbers N24, N25	Subtract 3-digit numbers N5, N7	Subtract 3- and 4-digit numbers N25
	Subtraction 3-digit numbers N30, N31	Subtract tenths (decimals) N21, N22	Subtract tenths and hundredths N12

Multiplication

Abacus 3	Abacus 4	Abacus 5	Abacus 6
Count in twos R3	Concept of multiplication R1, N4	Multiplication facts to 10 x 10 N8, N10	Multiplication facts to 10 × 10 N8
Multiply ×2, ×3, ×4, ×5, ×9, ×10 N7, N8, N9, N21, N22	Doubles N5	Multiply by 10 and 100 R5, N13	Multiply by 10, 100 and multiples of 10 and 100 N13, N30
	Multiply ×3, ×4, ×6, ×7, ×8, ×9 N8, N9, N10, N11, N26, N27	Multiply by 1-digit number N29, N30	Multiply by a 1-digit number N14, N31
			Multiply by a 2-digit number N15

Division

Abacus 3	Abacus 4	Abacus 5	Abacus 6
Equal share R6, N25	Grouping R5, N32	Grouping R4	Division facts to 100 N9
		Division facts to 100 N10	Divisibility rules N23
Links with multiplication N26	Remainders N33	Remainders N11	Division by a 1-digit number N27, N33
		Division by 1-digit number N31, N32	Division by 10, 100 and multiples of 10 N28, N32

Abacus 3	Abacus 4	Abacus 5	Abacus 6

References are to Teacher Cards within each year. AT1 of the National Curriculum and the use of calculators are an integral part of the course.

Fractions

Abacus 3	Abacus 4	Abacus 5	Abacus 6
Find halves, thirds, quarters and eighths N23, N24	Find halves, thirds, quarters and eighths R3, N12, N14	Tenths N15	
	Equivalent fractions N13	Fractions of amounts R6, N23	Fractions of amounts R4
	Mixed fractions N15	Equivalent fractions N24	Equivalent fractions N17
	Decimals N16	Hundredths N25, N26	
		Percentages N27	Percentages N18. N19

Data handling

Abacus 3	Abacus 4	Abacus 5	Abacus 6
Tally chart D1	Frequency table D1	Bar-line graphs D1	Pie chart D1
Bar graph D2	Bar graph D2	Frequency tables D3	Line graph D2, D3
Database D3	Database D3	Averages D2	Frequency table and histogram D4
Probability D4	Probability D4, D5	Probability D4, D5	Average D5
			Probability D6, D7

Measurement

Abacus 3	Abacus 4	Abacus 5	Abacus 6
Length dm, cm, m M1, M2	Length dm, cm, m M1	Length mm, cm, dm, m M1, M2	Length M1
Weight kg, g M7	Weight kg, g M4		Volume and capacity M3, M4
Capacity litre, half litre M4	Capacity ml, l M5		Area M6, M7
Capacity ml M5	Volume M6	Volume, cubic centimetre M3	Weight M2
Volume M6			Speed M2
Area M3	Area M2, M3	Area M4, M5	
Time five minutes R9, M8, M9	Time M7, M8, M9, M10	Time M6, M7, M8	

Shape

Abacus 3	Abacus 4	Abacus 5	Abacus 6
2-d shape S1, S2	2-d shape S1, S2	Perpendicular, parallel S1	2-d shape S1, S2
3-d shape S3, S4	3-d shape S3, S4	2-d shape (including circle) S2, S3	3-d shape S3
Symmetry S5	Rotation S5	3-d shape S4	Symmetry S4
Angle R10, S7, S8	Direction S6	Symmetry S5, S6	Angle S5, S6
Direction S6	Angle S7	Tessellation S7	Triangles S7, S8, S9
Position S9	Coordinates S8	Angle S8, S9	Coordinates S10
		Coordinates S10	